EASIEST
KEYBOARD
COLLECTION

Broadway

WISE PUBLICATIONS
London/New York/Paris/Sydney/Copenhagen/Madrid

Exclusive Distributors:

Music Sales Limited
8/9 Frith Street,
London W1V 5TZ, England.

Music Sales Pty Limited
120 Rothschild Avenue,
Rosebery, NSW 2018,
Australia.

Order No. AM952127
ISBN 0-7119-7288-5
This book © Copyright 1998 by Wise Publications

Book design by Chloë Alexander
Compiled by Peter Evans
Music arranged by Roger Day
Music processed by Paul Ewers Music Design

Printed in the United Kingdom by
Caligraving Limited, Thetford, Norfolk.

Cover photograph courtesy of Rex Features

Your Guarantee of Quality
As publishers, we strive to produce every book to the highest
commercial standards.
The music has been freshly engraved and the book has been carefully
designed to minimise awkward page turns and to make playing from
it a real pleasure.
Particular care has been given to specifying acid-free, neutral-sized
paper made from pulps which have not been elemental chlorine
bleached. This pulp is from farmed sustainable forests and was
produced with special regard for the environment.
Throughout, the printing and binding have been planned to ensure
a sturdy, attractive publication which should give years of enjoyment.
If your copy fails to meet our high standards, please inform us and
we will gladly replace it.

Music Sales' complete catalogue describes thousands of titles and is
available in full colour sections by subject, direct from Music Sales
Limited. Please state your areas of interest and send a cheque/postal
order for £1.50 for postage to: Music Sales Limited, Newmarket Road,
Bury St. Edmunds, Suffolk IP33 3YB.

Visit the Internet Music Shop at
http://www.musicsales.co.uk

Contents

ALL THE THINGS YOU ARE

Music by Jerome Kern
Words by Oscar Hammerstein II
© Copyright 1939 T.B. Harms & Company Incorporated, USA.
PolyGram Music Publishing Limited, 47 British Grove, London W4.
All Rights Reserved. International Copyright Secured.

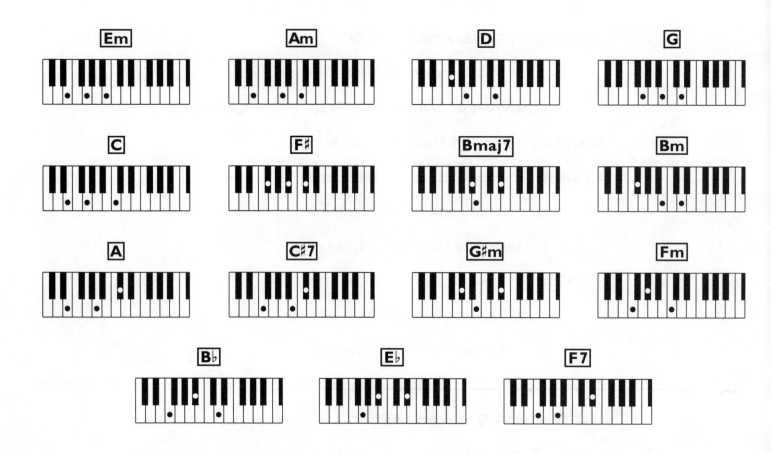

Voice: **Piano**

Rhythm: **Fox Trot**

Tempo: ♩ = 140

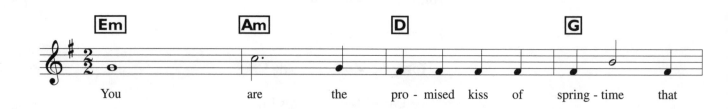

You are the pro-mised kiss of spring-time that

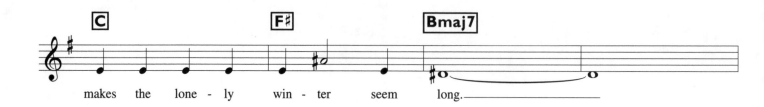

makes the lone-ly win-ter seem long.

4

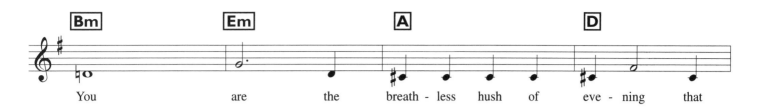

You are the breath-less hush of eve-ning that

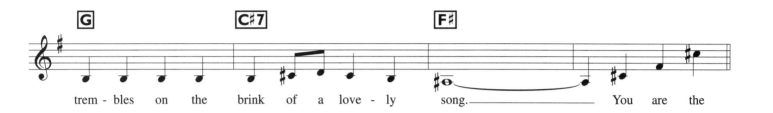

trem-bles on the brink of a love-ly song. You are the

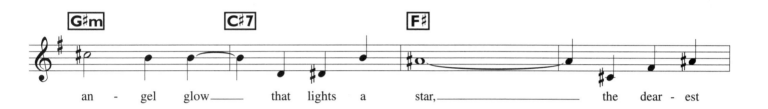

an - gel glow that lights a star, the dear-est

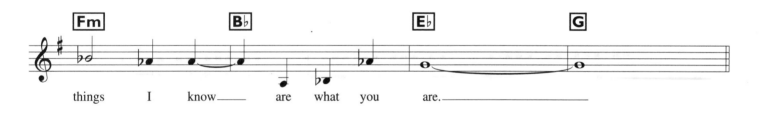

things I know are what you are.

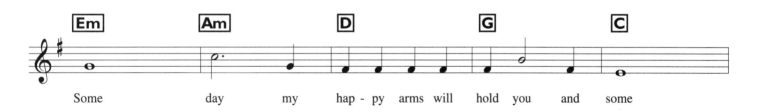

Some day my hap-py arms will hold you and some

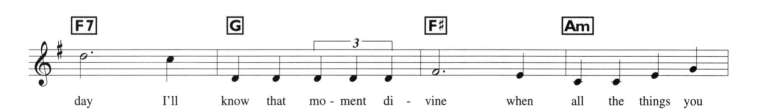

day I'll know that mo-ment di - vine when all the things you

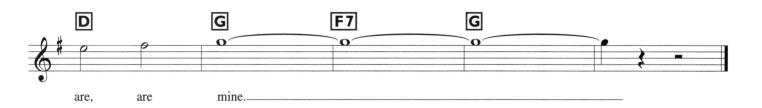

are, are mine.

ANOTHER SUITCASE IN ANOTHER HALL

Music by Andrew Lloyd Webber
Lyrics by Tim Rice

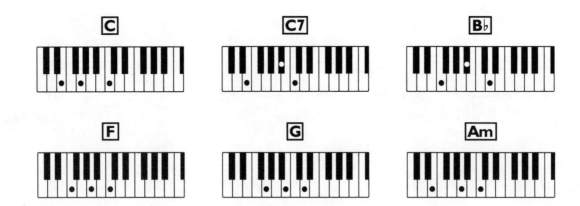

Voice: **Alto Sax**

Rhythm: **Soft Rock**

Tempo: ♩ = 76

don't   ex-pect   my   love af-fairs——   to   last   for   long,   ne-ver

fool   my-self   that   my   dreams——   will   come   true.

6

Be - ing used to trou - ble, I an - ti - ci - pate it, but

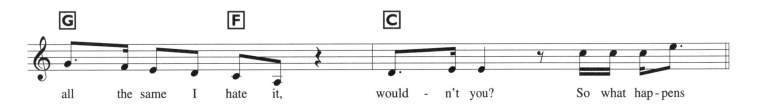

all the same I hate it, would - n't you? So what hap - pens

now? A - no - ther suit - case in a - no - ther hall,_____

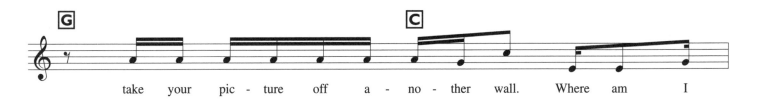

take your pic - ture off a - no - ther wall. Where am I

go - ing… you'll get by, you al - ways have be - fore. Where am I go - ing to?__

BIG SPENDER

Words by Dorothy Fields
Music by Cy Coleman
© Copyright 1965 by Dorothy Fields and Cy Coleman.
Rights assigned to Notable Music Company Incorporated in co-publication with Lida Enterprises Incorporated.
Campbell Connelly & Company Limited, 8/9 Frith Street, London W1.
All Rights Reserved. International Copyright Secured.

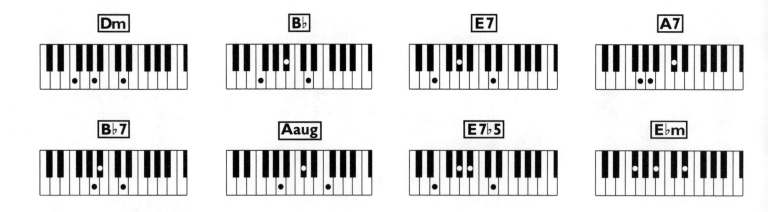

Voice: **Brass Ensemble**

Rhythm: **Big Band (Swing)**

Tempo: ♩ = 108

The mi - nute you walked in the joint

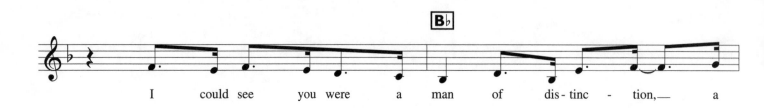

I could see you were a man of dis - tinc - tion,— a

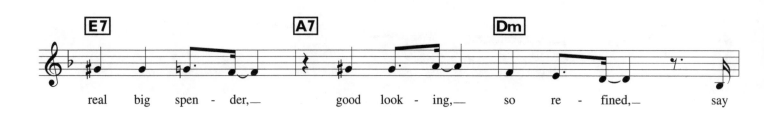

real big spen - der,— good look - ing,— so re - fined,— say

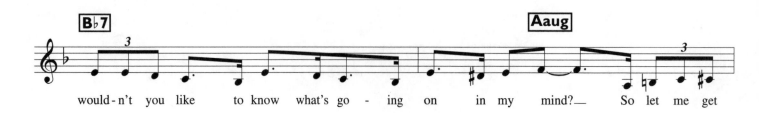

would - n't you like to know what's go - ing on in my mind?— So let me get

right to the point, I don't pop my cork for ev - 'ry guy I see.

Hey, big spen - der!

Hey, big spen - der! Hey, big spen - der!

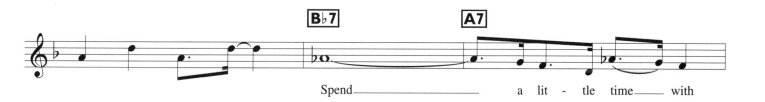

Spend a lit - tle time with

me. Spend a lit - tle time with

me. Spend a lit - tle time with

me.

BROTHERHOOD OF MAN

Words & Music by Frank Loesser

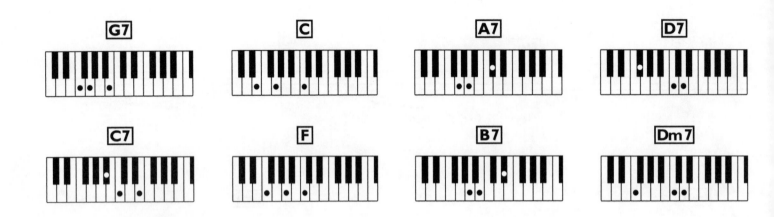

Voice: **Reed Organ**

Rhythm: **Township**

Tempo: ♩ = 124

There is a bro-ther-hood_____ of

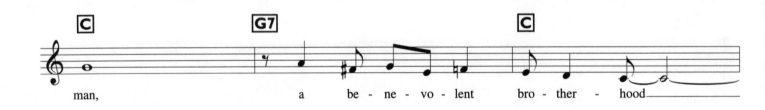

man, a be-ne-vo-lent bro-ther-hood_____

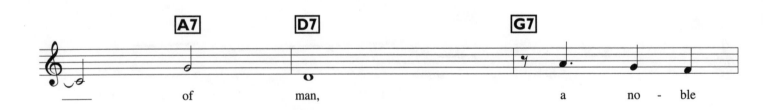

_____ of man, a no-ble

tie that binds___ all hu-man hearts and minds___

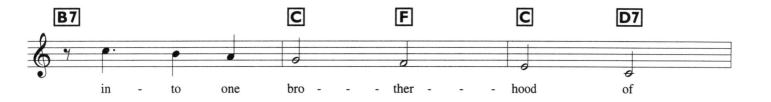

in - to one bro - - - ther - - - hood of

man. Your life - long mem - ber - ship

is free, keep a' giv - ing each

bro - ther all you can.

Oh aren't you proud to be in that fra -

- ter - ni - ty, the great big bro - - - ther - - -

- hood of man?

CAN'T HELP LOVIN' DAT MAN

Music by Jerome Kern
Words by Oscar Hammerstein II

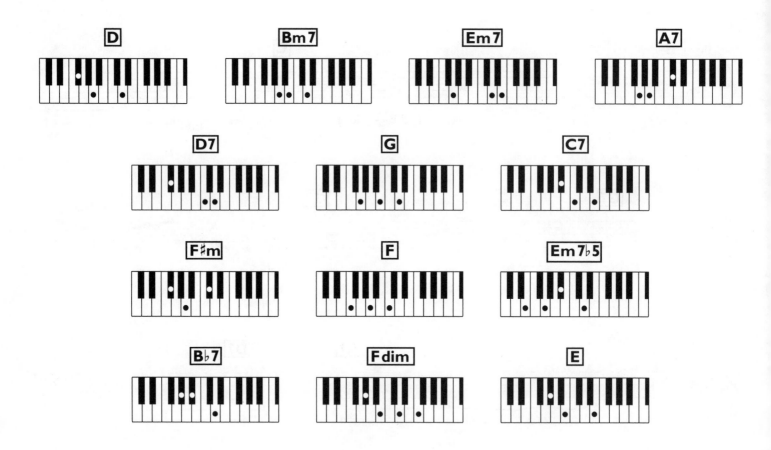

Voice: **French Horn**

Rhythm: **Slow Swing**

Tempo: ♩ = 120

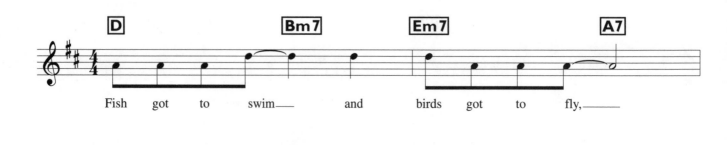

Fish got to swim—— and birds got to fly,——

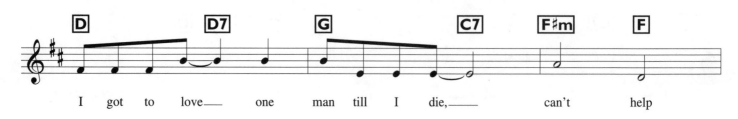

I got to love—— one man till I die,—— can't help

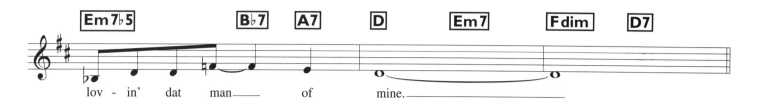

lov - in' dat man_____ of mine._____

When he goes a - way dat's a rain - y

day, and when he comes back dat day is

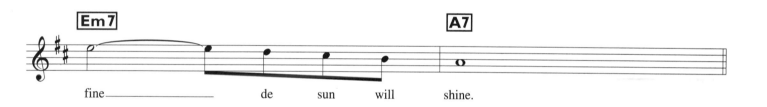

fine_____ de sun will shine.

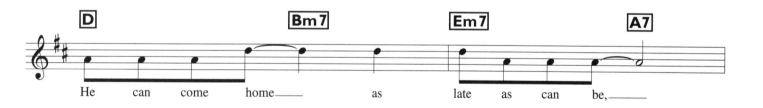

He can come home_____ as late as can be,_____

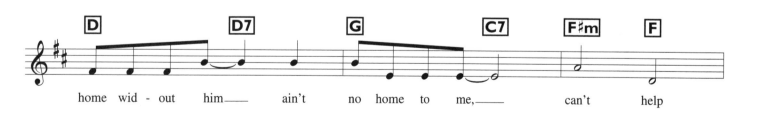

home wid - out him_____ ain't no home to me,_____ can't help

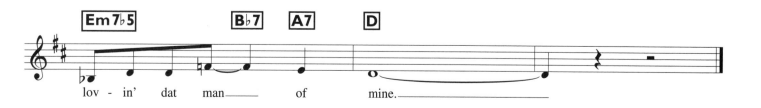

lov - in' dat man_____ of mine._____

EMPTY CHAIRS AT EMPTY TABLES

Music by Claude-Michel Schönberg
Lyrics by Herbert Kretzmer & Alain Boublil

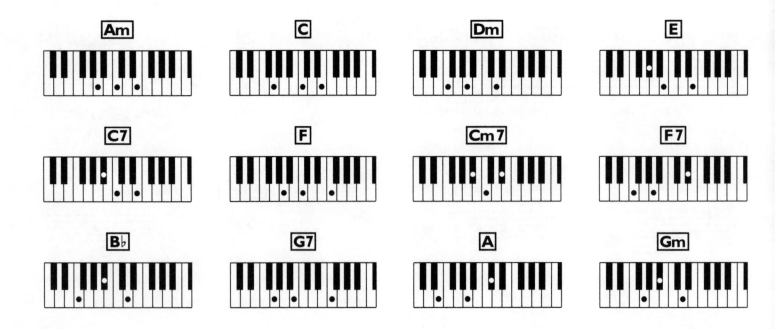

Voice: **12-string Guitar**

Rhythm: **Cha-cha**

Tempo: ♩ = 88

There's a grief that can't be spo - ken___ there's a pain goes on and on.___

Em - pty chairs and em - pty ta - bles, now my friends are dead and gone.

Here they talked of re - vo - lu - tion,___ here it was they lit the flame,___

here they sang a - bout to - mor-row and to - mor - row ne - ver came.

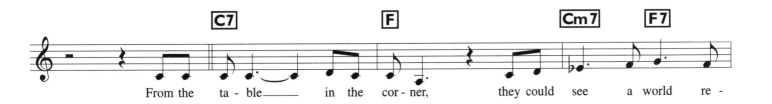

From the ta - ble_____ in the cor - ner, they could see a world re -

- born._____ And they rose with voi - ces ring - ing, I can hear them

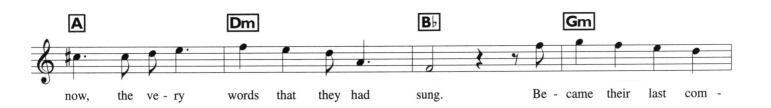

now, the ve - ry words that they had sung. Be - came their last com -

- mun - ion on the lone - ly bar - ri - cade at dawn.

Oh my friends, my friends for - give me,_____ that I live and you are gone,_____

there's a grief that can't be spo - ken, there's a pain goes on and on.

GONNA BUILD A MOUNTAIN

Words & Music by Leslie Bricusse & Anthony Newley

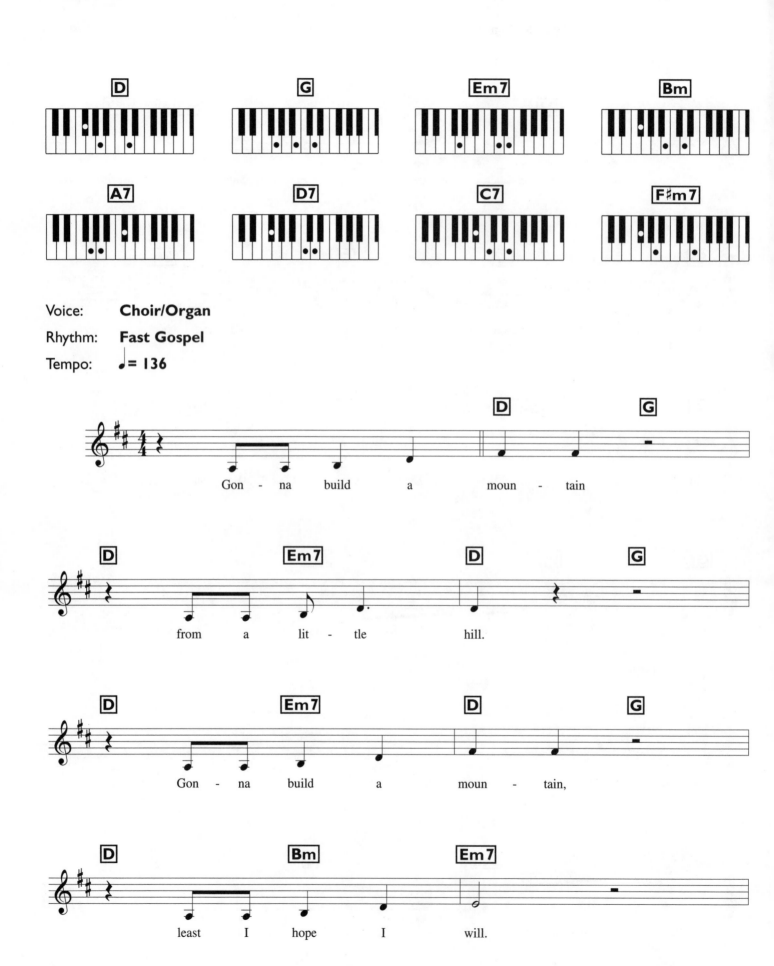

Voice: **Choir/Organ**

Rhythm: **Fast Gospel**

Tempo: ♩ = 136

Gon - na build a moun - tain, gon - na build it

high, I don't know how I'm gon - na do it,

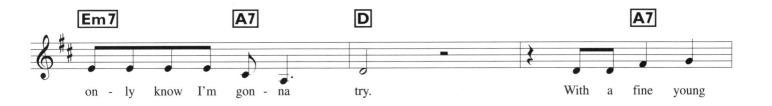

on - ly know I'm gon - na try. With a fine young

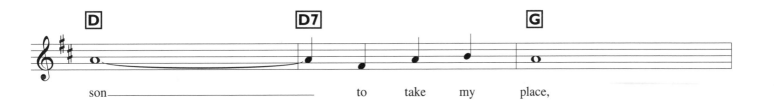

son _____ to take my place,

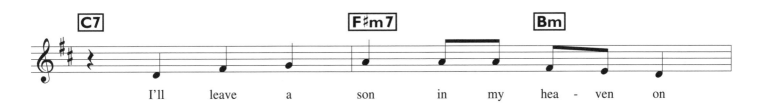

I'll leave a son in my hea - ven on

earth with the good Lord's grace. _____

17

GUYS AND DOLLS

Words & Music by Frank Loesser

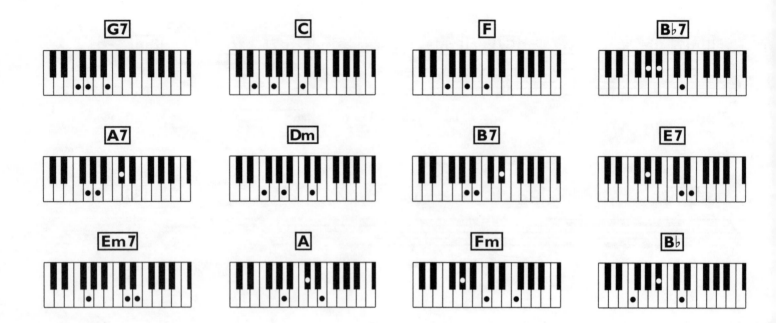

Voice: **Brass Ensemble**

Rhythm: **Fox Trot**

Tempo: ♩ = 160

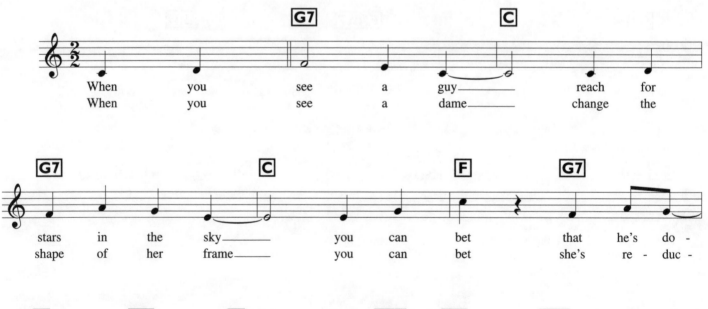

When you see a guy —— reach for
When you see a dame —— change for the

stars in the sky —— you can bet that he's do-
shape of her frame —— you can bet she's re-duc-

-ing it for some doll. When you spot a
-ing it for some guy. When you find a

I'VE TOLD EV'RY LITTLE STAR

Music by Jerome Kern
Words by Oscar Hammerstein II

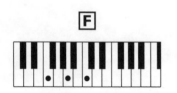
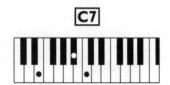
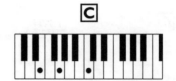
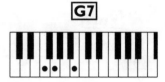

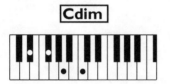
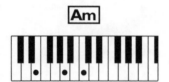
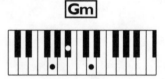

Voice: **Brass/Piano**

Rhythm: **Folky Pop**

Tempo: ♩ = 112

I've told ev-'ry lit-tle star, just how sweet I

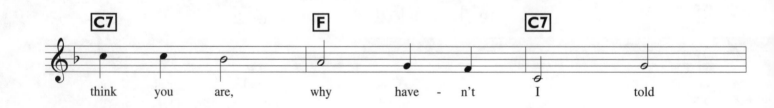

think you are, why have-n't I told

you? I've told rip-ples in a brook,

made my heart an op-en book, why have-n't

I told you?

Friends ask me, am I in love? I al - ways an - swer

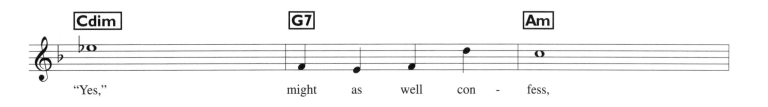

"Yes," might as well con - fess,

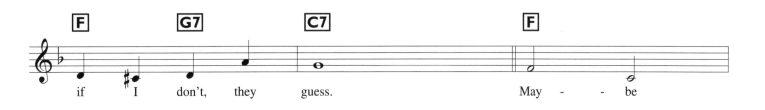

if I don't, they guess. May - - be

you may know it too, oh, my dar - ling, if you do,

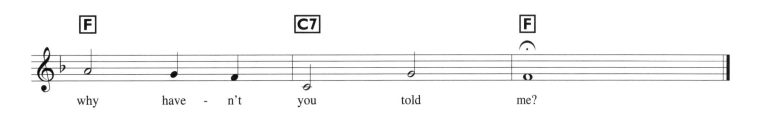

why have - n't you told me?

IF I WERE A BELL

Words & Music by Frank Loesser
© Copyright 1950 Frank Music Corporation, USA.
© Copyright renewed 1978 Frank Music Corporation.
Published & administered by MPL Communications Limited.
All Rights Reserved. International Copyright Secured.

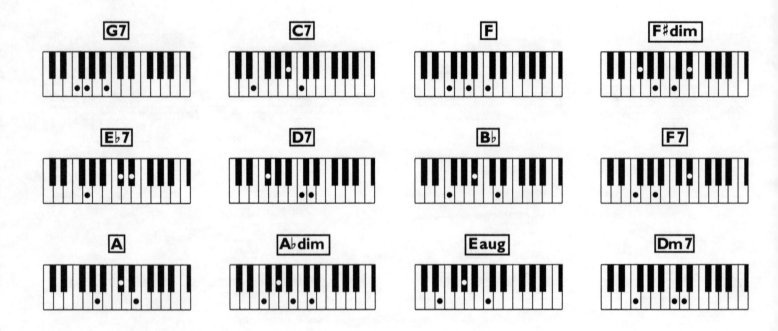

Voice: **Trumpet**

Rhythm: **Big Band**

Tempo: ♩ = 126

Ask me how do I feel,— ask me now that we're co - sy and

cling - ing.——— Well Sir, all I can say— is if I—

were a bell— I'd be ring - ing.——— From the

mo - ment we kissed to - night,— that's the way I've just got to be - have.— Boy if

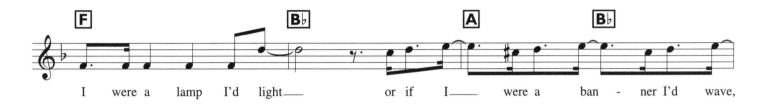

I were a lamp I'd light—— or if I—— were a ban - ner I'd wave,

—— ask me how do I feel,— lit - tle me with my qui - et up -

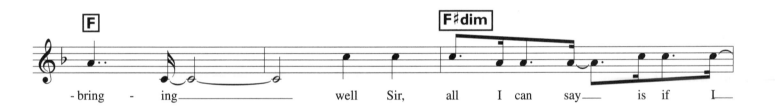

- bring - ing———————— well Sir, all I can say—— is if I—

—— were a gate—— I'd be swing - ing.——————— And if

I were a watch I'd start pop - ping my spring,———————— or if

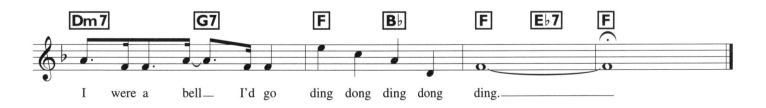

I were a bell— I'd go ding dong ding dong ding.————

OL' MAN RIVER

Music by Jerome Kern
Words by Oscar Hammerstein II

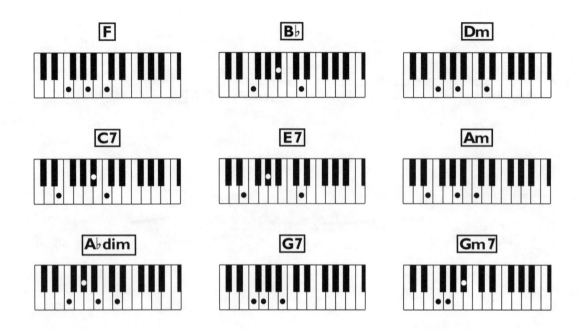

Voice: **Whistle**

Rhythm: **Folk**

Tempo: ♩ = 96

Ol' man ri - ver, dat ol' man ri - ver, he must know sump - in' but

don't say no - thin', he just keeps roll - in', he keeps on roll - in' a -

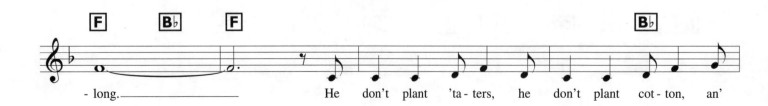

- long. He don't plant 'ta - ters, he don't plant cot - ton, an'

dem dat plants 'em is soon for - got - ten, but ol' man ri - ver, he

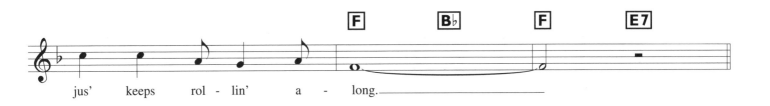

jus' keeps rol - lin' a - long._____

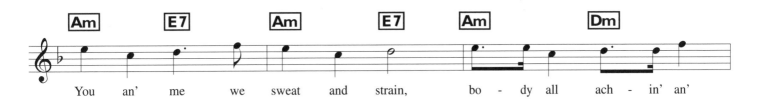

You an' me we sweat and strain, bo - dy all ach - in' an'

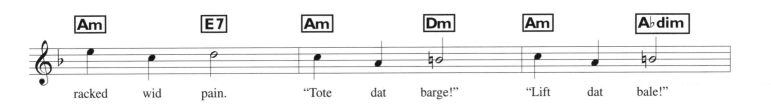

racked wid pain. "Tote dat barge!" "Lift dat bale!"

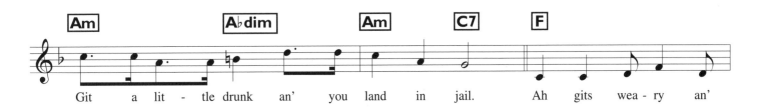

Git a lit - tle drunk an' you land in jail. Ah gits wea - ry an'

sick of try - in', ah'm tired of liv - in' an' skeered of dy - in' but

ol' man ri - ver, he jus' keeps rol - lin' a - long._____

ONCE IN LOVE WITH AMY

Words & Music by Frank Loesser

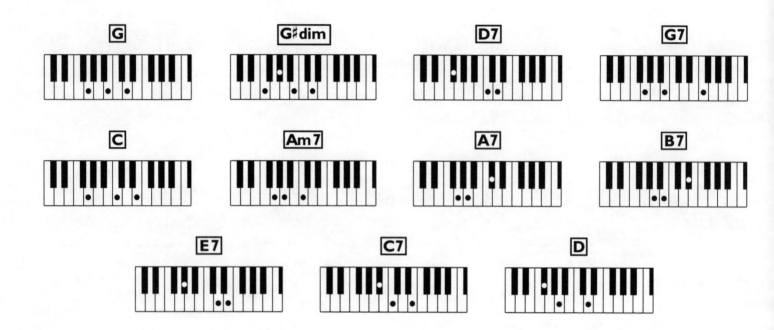

Voice: **Tuba**

Rhythm: **Swing**

Tempo: ♩ = 112

Once in love with A - my,＿＿ al - ways in love with

A - my,＿＿ ev - er and ev - er, fas - ci - na - ted by 'er,

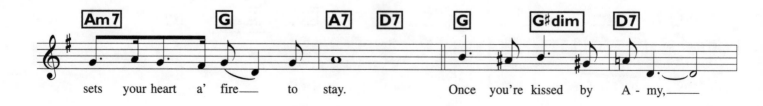

sets your heart a' fire＿ to stay. Once you're kissed by A - my,＿＿

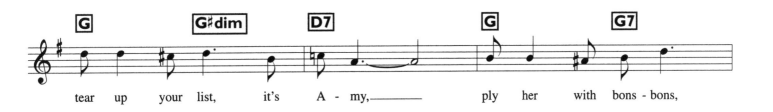

tear up your list, it's A - my,_____ ply her with bons - bons,

po - et - ry and flow - ers. moon a mil - lion hours___ a - way. You

might be quite the fic - kle heart - ed ro - ver, so care - free and bold, who

loves a girl and la - ter thinks it ov - er and just quits cold. But

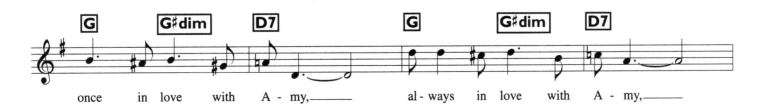

once in love with A - my,_____ al - ways in love with A - my,_____

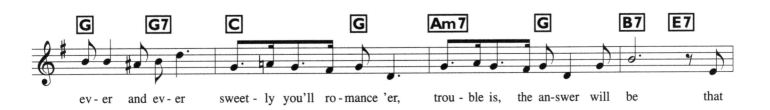

ev - er and ev - er sweet - ly you'll ro - mance 'er, trou - ble is, the an - swer will be that

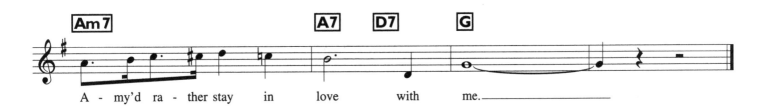

A - my'd ra - ther stay in love with me._____

ONE HAND, ONE HEART

Music by Leonard Bernstein
Lyrics by Stephen Sondheim

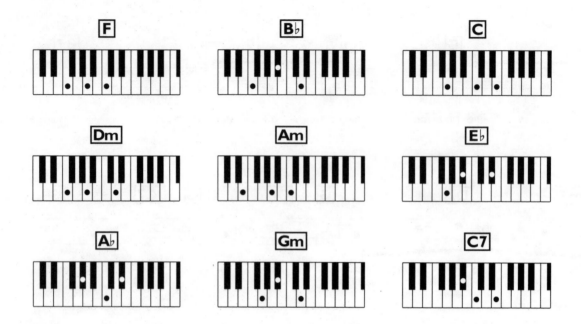

Voice: **Strings**

Rhythm: **Waltz**

Tempo: ♩ = 88

Make   of   our   hands,   one   hand.

Make   of   our   hearts,   one   heart.

Make   of   our   vows,   one   last   vow;

SIT DOWN, YOU'RE ROCKING THE BOAT

Words & Music by Frank Loesser
© Copyright 1950 Frank Music Corporation, USA.
© Copyright renewed 1978 Frank Music Corporation.
Published & administered by MPL Communications Limited.
All Rights Reserved. International Copyright Secured.

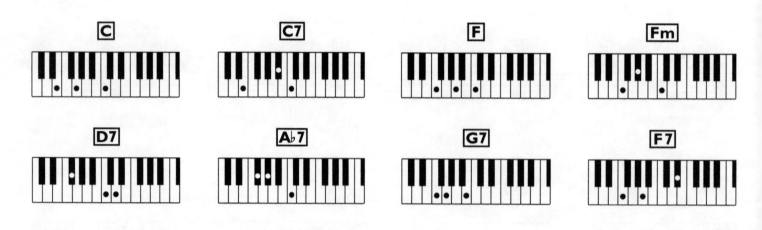

Voice: **'Ooh'**

Rhythm: **Chicago Blues**

Tempo: ♩ = 136

For the peo - ple all said "sit down,— sit down

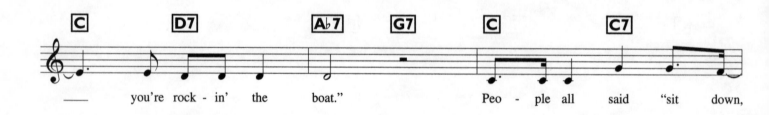

— you're rock - in' the boat." Peo - ple all said "sit down,

— sit down— you're rock - in' the boat."— And the

de - vil will drag you un - der by the sharp la - pel— of your

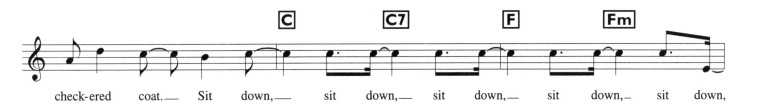

check-ered coat.— Sit down,— sit down,— sit down,— sit down,— sit down,

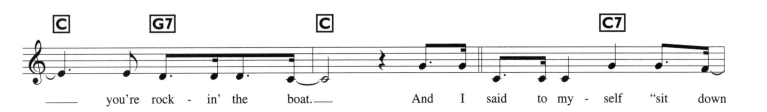

—— you're rock - in' the boat.— And I said to my - self "sit down

—— sit down,— you're rock - in' the boat."

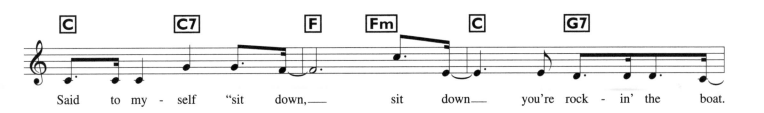

Said to my - self "sit down,— sit down— you're rock - in' the boat.

—— And the de - vil will drag you un - der with a

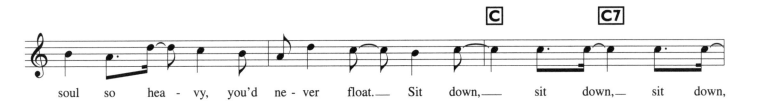

soul so hea - vy, you'd ne - ver float.— Sit down,— sit down,— sit down,

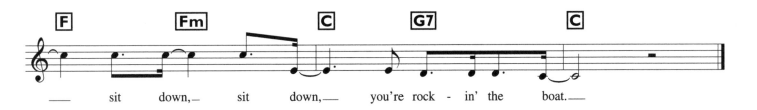

—— sit down,— sit down,— you're rock - in' the boat.——

STANDING ON THE CORNER

Words & Music by Frank Loesser

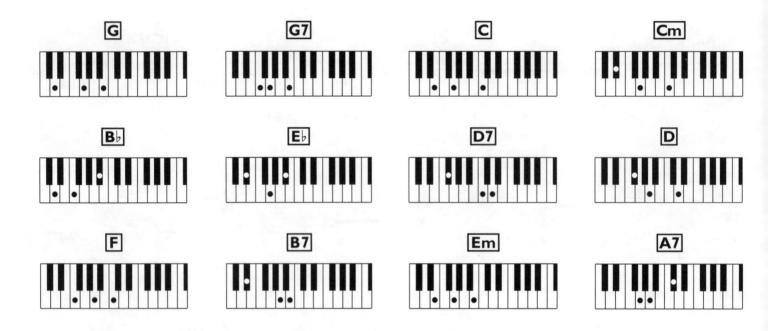

Voice: **Acoustic Guitar**

Rhythm: **Swing**

Tempo: ♩ = 120

Stand - ing on the cor - ner watch - ing all the girls go by.

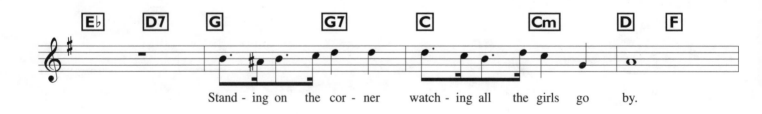

Stand - ing on the cor - ner watch - ing all the girls go by.

Bro - ther you don't know a ni - cer oc - cu - pa - tion, mat - ter of

SUNRISE SUNSET

Words by Sheldon Harnick
Music by Jerry Bock

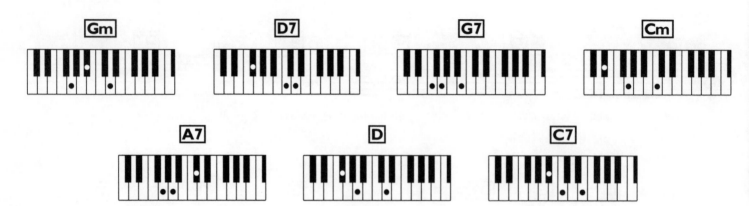

Voice: **Clarinet**

Rhythm: **Waltz**

Tempo: ♩ = 132

When did she get to be a beau - - - -

- ty? When did he grow to be so

tall? Was - n't it

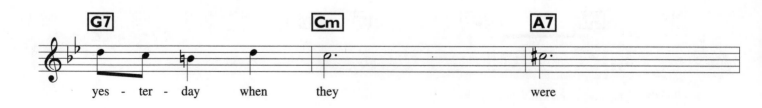

yes - ter - day when they were

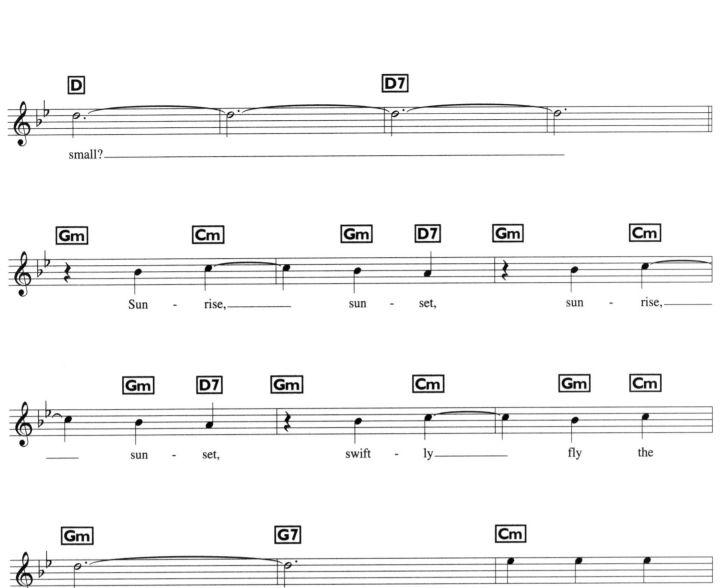

small?

Gm   Cm   Gm   D7   Gm   Cm

Sun - rise,_____ sun - set, sun - rise,_____

Gm   D7   Gm   Cm   Gm   Cm

_____ sun - set, swift - ly_____ fly the

Gm   G7   Cm

years._____ One sea - son

D7   Gm   C7

fol - low - ing an - oth - - - - - er,

Cm   D7

la - - - den with hap - pi - ness and

Gm

tears._____

THE IMPOSSIBLE DREAM

Music by Mitch Leigh
Words by Joe Darion

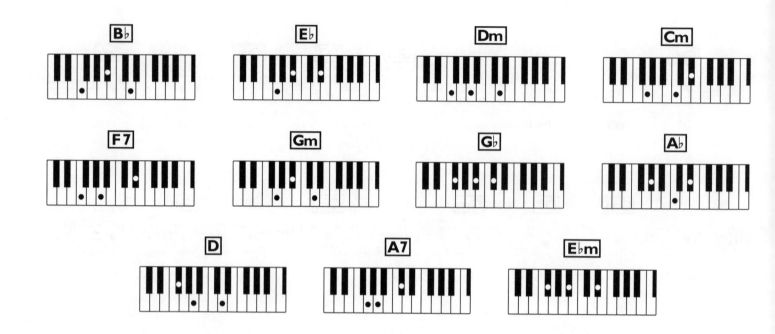

Voice: **Trumpet**

Rhythm: **Waltz**

Tempo: ♩ = 72

To dream——— the im - pos - si - ble dream, to

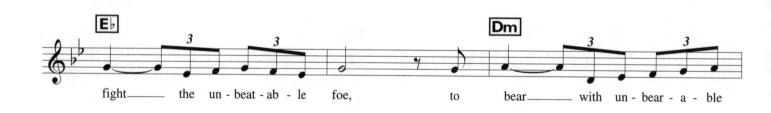

fight——— the un - beat - ab - le foe, to bear——— with un - bear - a - ble

sor - row——— to run——— where the brave dare not go. This is my

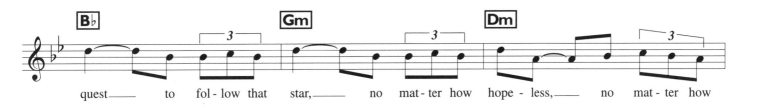

quest____ to fol-low that star,____ no mat-ter how hope-less,____ no mat-ter how

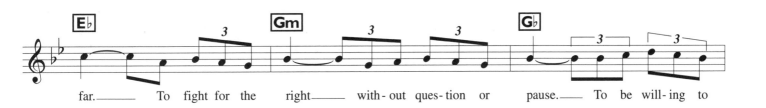

far.____ To fight for the right____ with-out ques-tion or pause.____ To be will-ing to

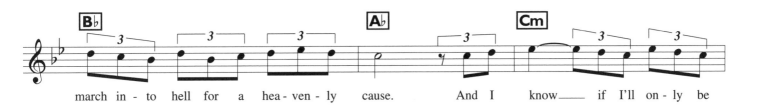

march in-to hell for a hea-ven-ly cause. And I know____ if I'll on-ly be

true____ to the glo-ri-ous quest, that my heart____ will be peace-ful and

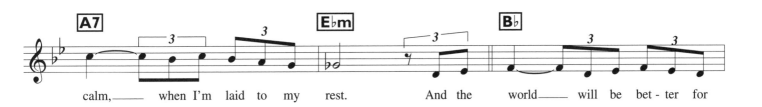

calm,____ when I'm laid to my rest. And the world____ will be bet-ter for

this,____ that one man____ scorned and cov-ered with scars____ still

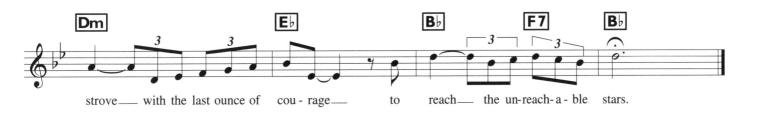

strove__ with the last ounce of cou-rage___ to reach__ the un-reach-a-ble stars.

THE SONG IS YOU

Music by Jerome Kern
Words by Oscar Hammerstein II

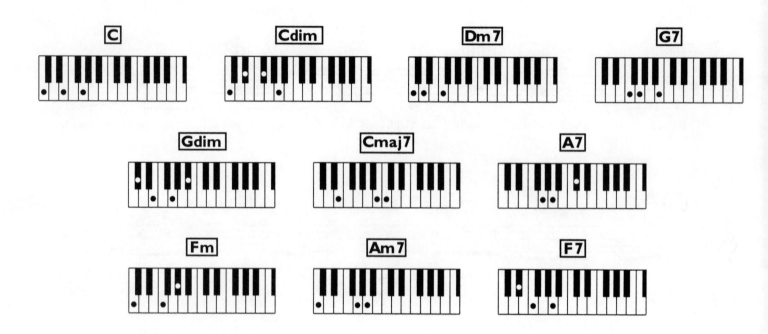

Voice: **Clarinet**

Rhythm: **Fox Trot**

Tempo: ♩ = 116

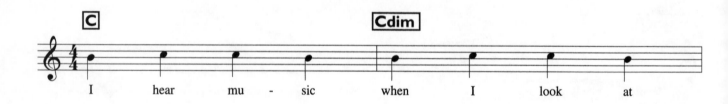

I hear mu - sic when I look at

you, _____ a beau - ti - ful theme of ev - 'ry

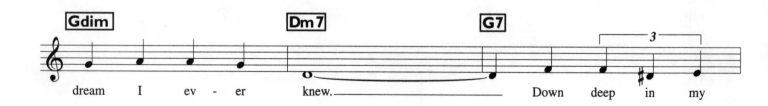

dream I ev - er knew. _____ Down deep in my

heart _____ I hear it play, _____ I feel it

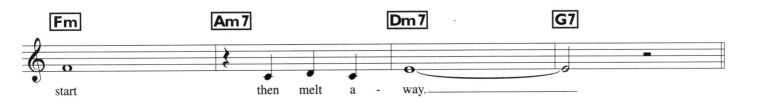

start   then melt a - way. _____

I   hear   mu - sic   when   I   touch   your   hand. _____

___   A   beau - ti - ful   me - lo - dy   from   some   en - chant - ed

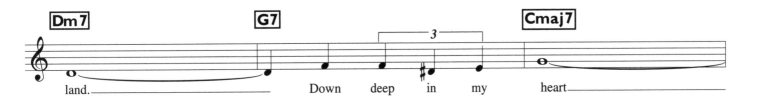

land. _____   Down   deep   in   my   heart _____

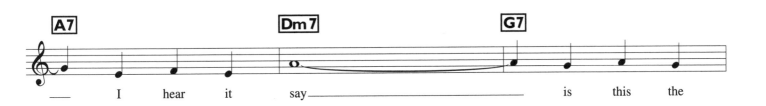

___   I   hear   it   say _____   is   this   the

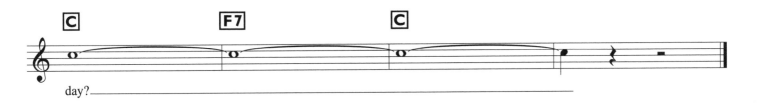

day? _____

'TIL TOMORROW

Music by Jerry Bock
Lyrics by Sheldon Harnick

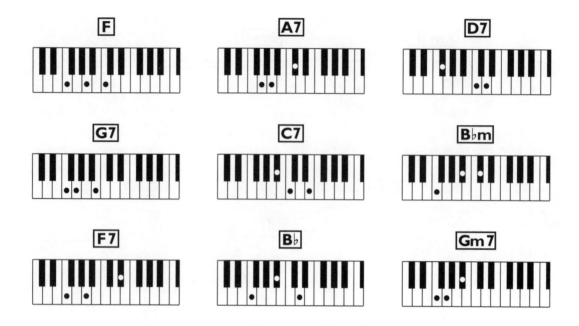

Voice: **Piano**

Rhythm: **Waltz**

Tempo: ♩ = 132

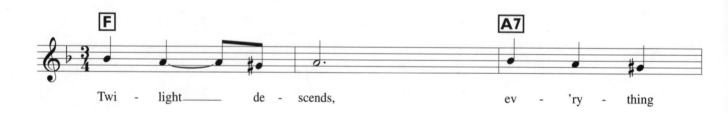

Twi - light___ de - scends, ev - 'ry - thing

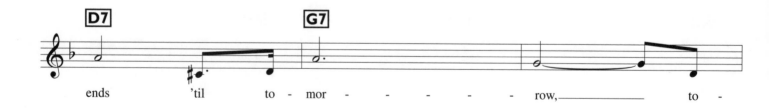

ends 'til to - mor - - - - - row,___ to -

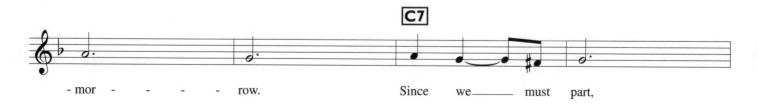

- mor - - - - row. Since we___ must part,

TOMORROW

Music by Charles Strouse
Words by Martin Charnin

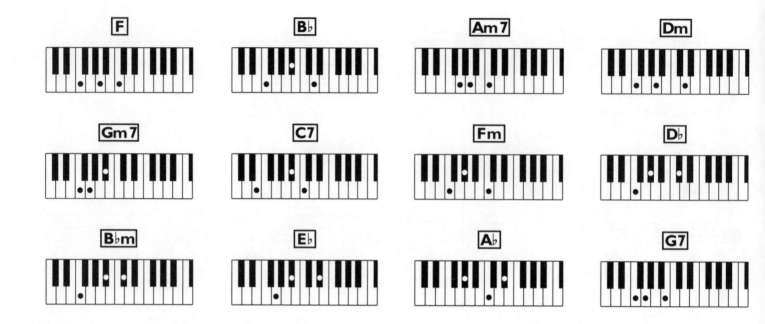

Voice: **Trumpet**

Rhythm: **Epic Ballad**

Tempo: ♩ = 78

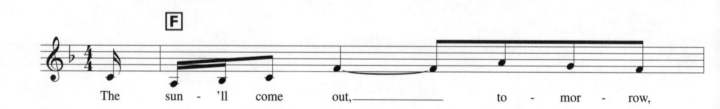

The sun - 'll come out,_____ to - mor - row,

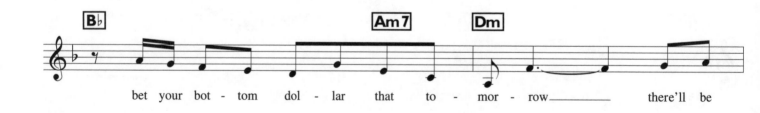

bet your bot - tom dol - lar that to - mor - row_____ there'll be

sun!   Jus' think - ing a - bout_____ to - mor - row

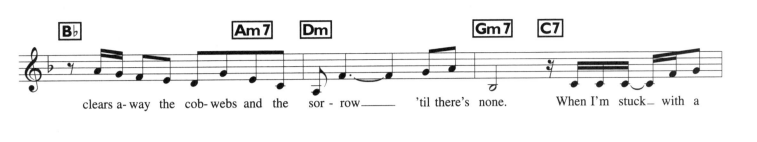

clears a-way the cob-webs and the sor - row_____ 'til there's none. When I'm stuck__ with a

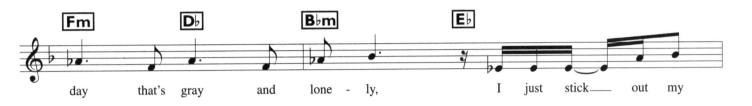

day that's gray and lone - ly, I just stick_____ out my

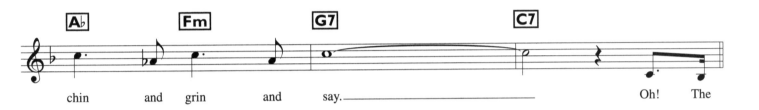

chin and grin and say._____ Oh! The

sun-'ll come out_____ to - mor - row, so you got to hang on 'til to - mor - row _____ come what

may! To - mor - row, to - mor - row, I love ya, to - mor - row, you're

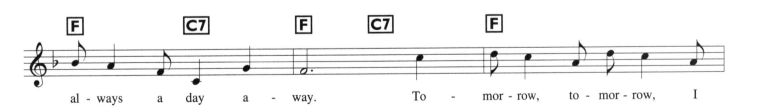

al - ways a day a - way. To - mor - row, to - mor - row, I

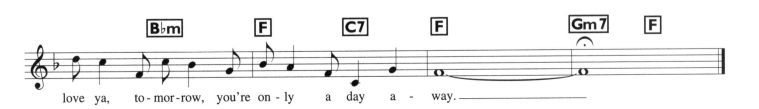

love ya, to - mor-row, you're on - ly a day a - way._____

TONIGHT

Music by Leonard Bernstein
Lyrics by Stephen Sondheim

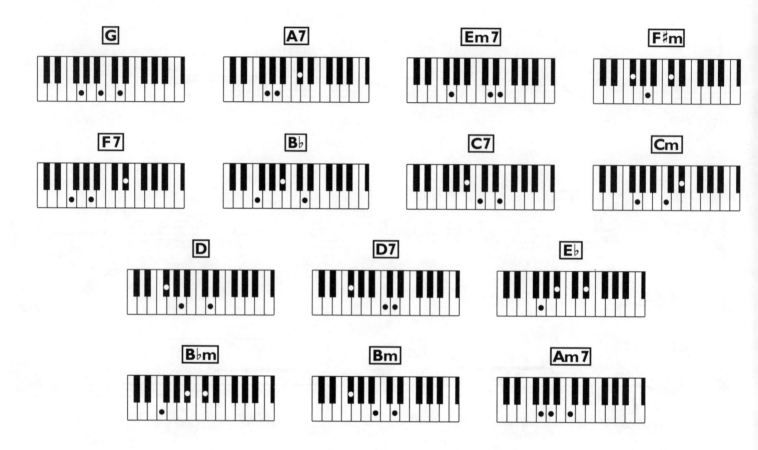

Voice: **French Horn**

Rhythm: **Bolero**

Tempo: ♩ = 116

To - night, to - night, won't be just a - ny night, to -

- night there will be no morn - ing star. _____ To -

WHAT I DID FOR LOVE

Words by Edward Kleban
Music by Marvin Hamlisch

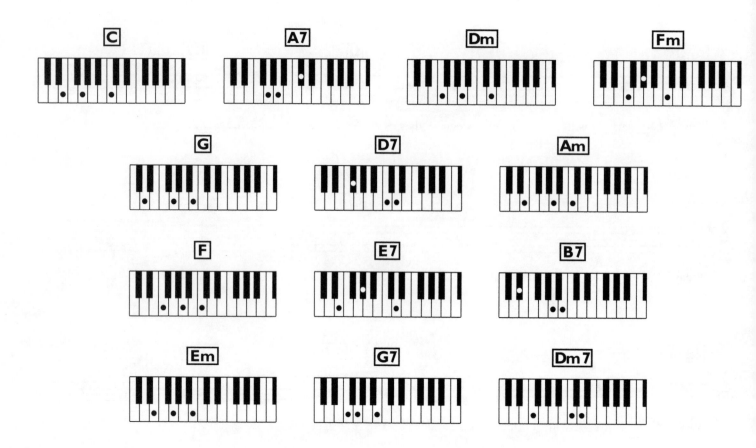

Voice: **Alto Sax**

Rhythm: **Pop Ballad**

Tempo: ♩= 108

Kiss to-day good-bye,   the sweet-ness and the sor-row,——

wish me luck, the same to you,   but I can't re-

46

- gret what I did for love,_____ what I did for love.

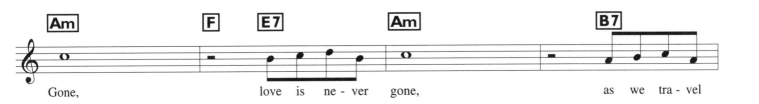

Gone, love is ne - ver gone, as we tra - vel

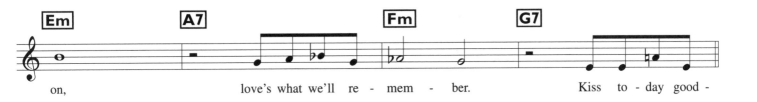

on, love's what we'll re - mem - ber. Kiss to - day good -

- bye and point me t'ward to - mor - row,_____

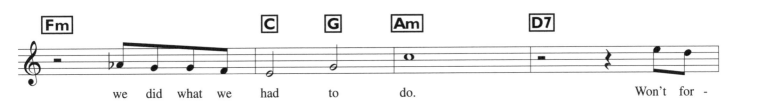

we did what we had to do. Won't for -

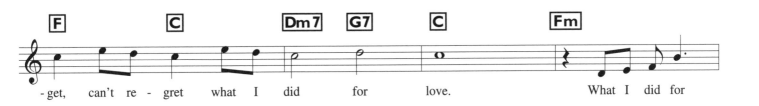

- get, can't re - gret what I did for love. What I did for

love, what I did for love._____

EASIEST KEYBOARD COLLECTION

Easy-to-play melody line arrangements for all keyboards with chord symbols and lyrics. Suggested registration, rhythm and tempo are included for each song together with keyboard diagrams showing left-hand chord voicings used.

  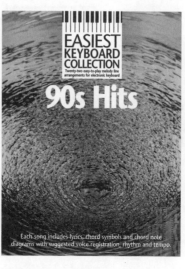 

Showstoppers

Consider Yourself (Oliver!), Do You Hear The People Sing? (Les Misérables), I Know Him So Well (Chess), Maria (West Side Story), Smoke Gets In Your Eyes (Roberta) and 17 more big stage hits.
Order No. AM944218

Pop Classics

A Whiter Shade Of Pale (Procol Harum), Bridge Over Troubled Water (Simon & Garfunkel), Crocodile Rock (Elton John) and nineteen more classic pop hits, including Hey Jude (The Beatles), Imagine (John Lennon), Massachusetts (The Bee Gees) and Stars (Simply Red).
Order No. AM944196

90s Hits

Over twenty of the greatest hits of the 1990s, including Always (Bon Jovi), Fields Of Gold (Sting), Have I Told You Lately (Rod Stewart), One Sweet Day (Mariah Carey), Say You'll Be There (Spice Girls), and Wonderwall (Oasis).
Order No. AM944229

TV Themes

Twenty-two great themes from popular TV series, including Casualty, EastEnders, Gladiators, Heartbeat, I'm Always Here (Baywatch), Red Dwarf and The Black Adder.
Order No. AM944207

Also available...

Film Themes, Order No. AM952050   **Chart Hits**, Order No. AM952083
Jazz Classics, Order No. AM952061   **Classical Themes**, Order No. AM952094
Classic Blues, Order No. AM950697   **Christmas**, Order No. AM952105
Love Songs, Order No. AM950708   **Ballads**, Order No. AM952116
Pop Hits, Order No. AM952072   **Broadway**, Order No. AM952127